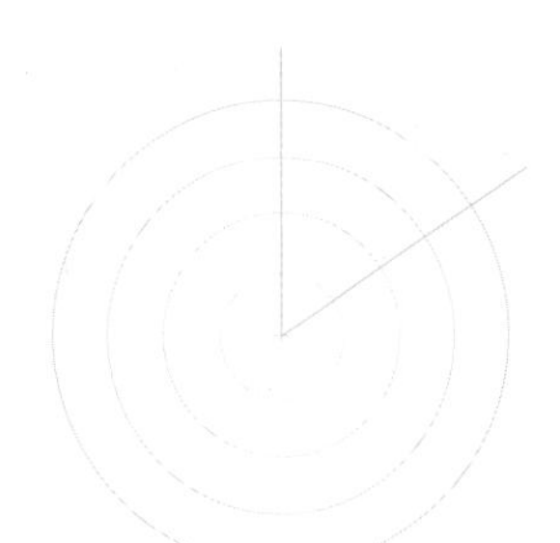

Addendum to the Second Edition of The Radar Book

Introduction

In the eight years since publication of the 2nd Edition of *The Radar Book*, the world of marine electronics has been turned on its head. Technology which we could only dream about just a few years ago is now commonplace; some tried and true techniques of navigation and collision avoidance are no longer relevant and have been replaced by new techniques for new technology. And there is no reason to believe that this process will stop or even slow down in the near future.

Today, the old (but reliable) magnetron-based radars are being replaced by modern radars with solid state microwave signal generation; continuous-wave radars with a minimum range-scale of 200 feet (60 metres); and pulse compression and Doppler radars. As a result, radars consume far less power than just a few short years ago, they are as finely tuned as lasers, and their transmissions are far less intense.

At the same time, navigation has been enhanced by the integration of various technologies such as AIS, electronic charts, GPS, MARPA (Mini Automatic Radar Plotting Aid), tide, current and weather software, and the processing power of modern multi-function displays. This integration has developed to such a degree that it is no longer possible to discuss radar, without also considering the integration of all these other systems with the radar.

Finally, the incredible processing power available to manufacturers has made it possible not only to integrate all these technologies seamlessly, but also to process the returning radar echoes to extract detail never before possible.

These three areas of development have changed the face of navigation, and will continue to do so for the foreseeable future.

Primary Uses of Radar

For Collision Avoidance

Radar is a primary aid in collision avoidance situations. Radar will show you, the skipper, where the other vessel is in real time, night or day in good visibility or the thickest pea-soup fog you have ever seen. But its value doesn't end there. You can also use it to predict where the other vessel will be in the immediate future, to help you decide what avoiding action to take, and for monitoring the developing situation to determine if you made the right choice.

As a Navigation Aid

Radar is also a valuable navigational aid. Though it has fallen out of favour as a navigation tool in recent years, due to the use of chart plotters, radar remains a highly effective tool for navigating. Using just a few simple techniques, radar can be relied on for safe and confident navigation.

The combination of radar and electronic charts, AIS, and tide and current data in an integrated and dynamic presentation on a modern Multi-Function Display results in a user-friendly navigational environment, which is intuitive to use and is highly accurate. As a result, most coastal navigators have grown to depend on the integrated systems and no longer consider radar as a separate navigational tool.

Bluewater sailors find that in much of North America and Europe, the quality of the official electronic navigation charts is excellent, both in raster and vector format. This is why boaters in the developed world have come to depend on the seamless integration of charts and radar/GPS—and this is a reasonable approach in well charted waters. However, when they venture to other waters, they begin to discover that the charts may be significantly undependable. And it does not take a very large degree of error in the chart (or any particular element) and the integrated nature of the system becomes an Achilles heel, and your ability to navigate confidently is compromised.

Consequently, the prudent skipper will also ensure that:

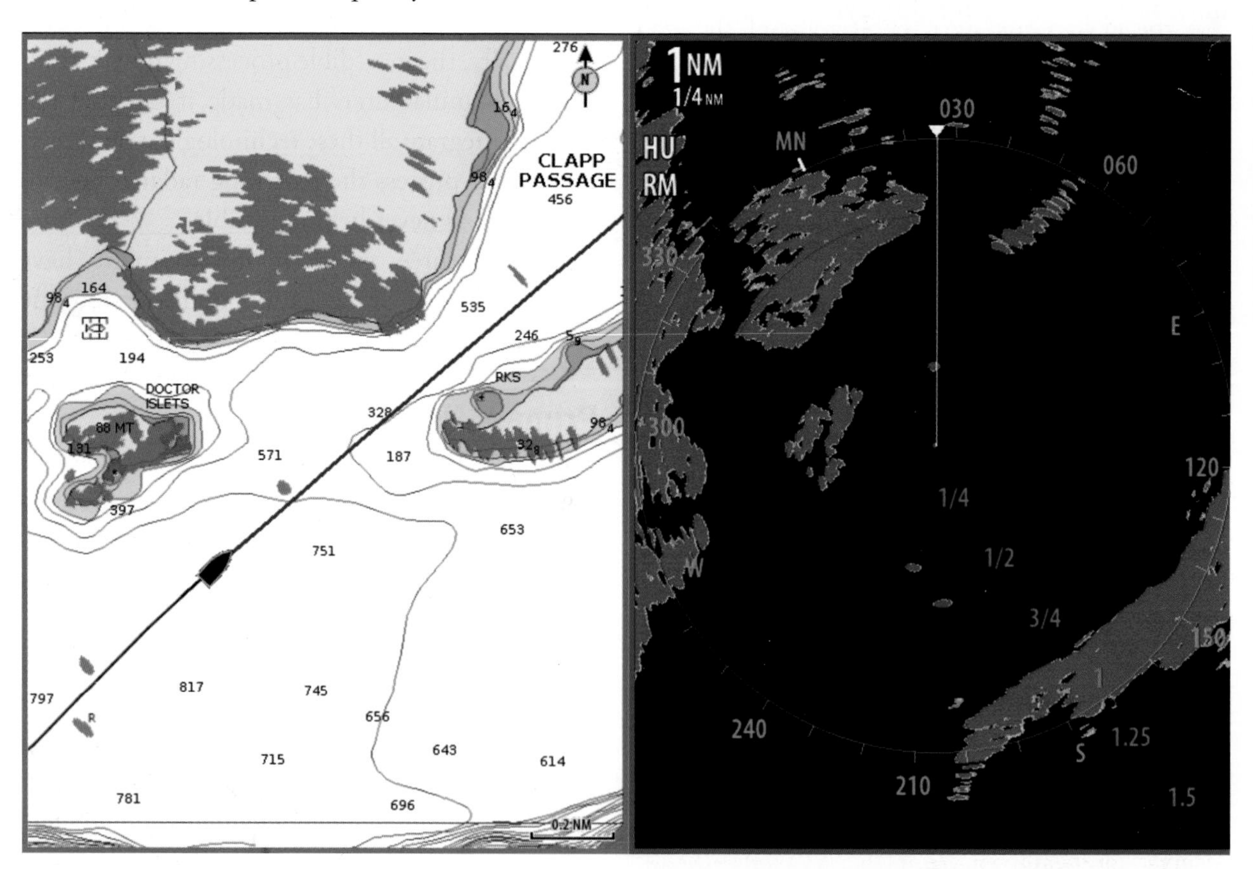

▲ Fig. 1

MFD Fails to Transfer All Radar Data

Some MFDs will overlay the basic radar imagery on the chart, but fail to transfer additional imagery, such as range rings. Without range rings, there are no intuitive cues to the scale of the chart, except the small distance scale at the bottom right. So you may have to display the radar image anyway. The problem is that now the images are half-size. *Screencapture of Simrad NSS 12 MFD & 4G radar*

- they understand how to get the most out of their integrated navigation system,
- they can recognize when the system components cease to work together, and
- they are able to compensate by using the radar for basic navigational tasks as well.

Multi-Function Displays (MFDs)

(Reference page 108 of the 2nd Edition)

There are many circumstances in which it is essential to be able to revert to a pure radar display when the screen is obscured by too much information. The problem is that many boats only have one MFD for displaying images. This may be due to the cost, or it may be due to a lack of space. Boaters are always having to compromise, and this is one circumstance in which they often do so.

If you have but a single MFD, you may be tempted to display the pure radar image as a small window on the larger display of the MFD. But when it has to compete for space with other displays, such as engine logging, engine room cameras, and electronic chart displays, this may mean that the radar imagery is very small and detail hard to see.

Certain MFDs don't allow the range rings and other features such as Electronic Bearing Lines and Variable Range Markers to appear as part of the radar overlay. This robs you of some very valuable cues for determining relative distance, scale of the display etc. If your software makes it possible, place a 0.1 Nm circle around your vessel in the charting program. This will provide valuable cues for estimating scale. If this is not possible, you will want to show the radar display as well as the chart with radar overlay, but if you have a single MFD, this means that both images are smaller than optimum.

Ideal Installation

The ideal display setup would be two completely separate MFDs. Either MFD could be reverted to a pure radar display for collision avoidance purposes, while leaving the other display free to display electronic charts (with or without overlay). AIS could be displayed on both displays and MARPA as well if possible.

I have never found a boater who claims they never had to make compromises on board their boats, especially in the arrangement of their wheelhouses. So it is likely that many boaters would find it difficult to position two full size MFDs on their consoles. The problem is even more severe on sailing vessels that lack an enclosed bridge.

One option is to install a single MFD, and rely on a tablet with a navigation program for a

Fig. 2 ►
An Ideal Installation
An ideal installation would involve two complete MFDs, to which any sensor could be directed in any combination. In general one display would be reserved for radar without charts, and the other display would display the charts, with or without radar overlay.
Photo of Furuno dual MFD installation on MV Mana Kai (Jeff and Darlene Gidley) by Kevin Monahan

Fig. 3 ►
Tablet as a Second MFD
In this installation, the primary Simrad MFD is set to pure radar imagery, and the secondary iPad is loaded with the navigation software. GPS and AIS are supplied wirelessly by a Vesper XB-8000 Class B AIS Transponder (inset)
Photo of Simrad NSS-12 MFD and iPad on MV Safe Harbour (Sam Landsman) by Kevin Monahan
Inset photo courtesy Vesper Marine

secondary display, receiving GPS and AIS data from a wireless source. Under normal conditions, the MFD would display chart data with radar overlay, or a pure radar image. When it is necessary to switch the MFD to pure radar mode, the tablet is still able to display the navigation software, charts, AIS etc. In addition, the tablet can be slaved to the radar / MFD (most modern MFDs allow this function), providing the ability to monitor the electronics from another location such as the cockpit or flying bridge.

Until a short time ago, the trend in the industry has been to base integrated systems on a single Multi-Function Display which receives data from a number of different sensors (radar, GPS, AIS, depth sounder, etc). The MFD itself contained the electronic charts and navigation software, in addition to other software such as MARPA. As the MFD evolved through multiple incarnations, it had fewer and fewer knobs and buttons and began to be dependent on touch-screen technology. This was because knobs and switches are expensive, whereas software is cheap when mass produced.

However, the end result was an MFD that was entirely dependent on touch screens, with almost every function buried in a menu tree. And this presented its own problems. As knobs and switches were eliminated and their functions given to menus, the MFD became less user-friendly—an ironic twist for a technology that was supposed to make the interface more user-friendly.

Software designers often do not think like the equipment user. Very common functions may be buried several layers deep in a menu tree, while

Touchscreens

Touch-screens can be very difficult to use when the deck is moving beneath your feet. On one occasion I was trying to place the cursor in a very specific location in order to set a waypoint. We were heading into gale-force winds and the boat was very lively. In order to place the cursor where I wanted it I had to stand beside the MFD and hug it tightly to my body, while slowly and deliberately poking my finger where I wanted the cursor to go. The MFD had no roller ball or rocker switch for moving the cursor, so I had to rely on the touch-screen alone. It took more than two minutes to place the cursor where I wanted it to go.

Following this encounter with misguided technology, I have decided that touch-screens can be useful, but there must always be another mechanism for moving the cursor, EBL or VRM.

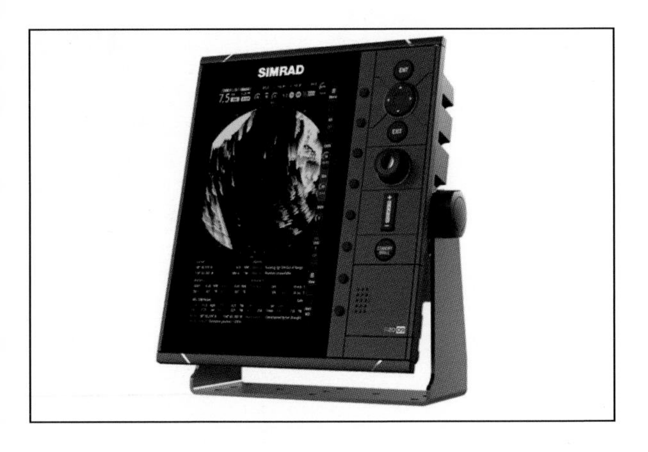

◄ **Fig. 4**
A Simrad R2009 Radar Control Unit
This control unit is available in a 9-inch (portrait) or a 16-inch (widescreen) version. Where space is at a premium, the 9-inch version makes a valuable addition to an existing MFD.
Photo courtesy Navico Corporation

uncommon functions are easy to access. It is also a sad truth; that the standard terminology used for control functions (page 75 and 76 of the 2nd Edition) has been supplanted by manufacturer-specific jargon, and the organization of menus sometimes becomes completely non-intuitive.

There have even been suggestions that the proliferation of menus has made navigation and collision avoidance more difficult, and more than one accident has been blamed in part on the difficulty of managing menus.

It's not surprising therefore, to see that at least one manufacturer has produced a "dedicated radar control unit" consisting of a display, and enough associated knobs and soft keys to easily control the many functions of radar. When connected by Ethernet or WiFi to a compatible antenna, it is reminiscent of a stand-alone radar. But this module is far more flexible; it can be connected by Ethernet to the radar scanner and another MFD and be a true part of an integrated navigation system.

NMEA 2000

Until the most recent generation of radars and MFDs, it seemed that NMEA 2000 was the ideal mechanism for distributing data from various sensors to MFDs. However, NMEA 2000 lacked the capacity to handle information-rich radar data. So NMEA 2000 needed to be supplemented by Ethernet or other proprietary data-sharing systems. Recently though, manufacturers are beginning to use Ethernet for data sharing between components—in fact some of the newer models are using WiFi to communicate between components, which makes installation a snap and allows for very inventive arrangements of displays on the bridge.

The end result is more flexibility in locating and interfacing equipment, and that adds up to a big win for the user.

Radar Overlay

(Reference page 110 of the 2nd Edition)
The overlay of radar on electronic charts has been a feature of many radar systems for several years now. But in recent years, electronic chart systems with radar overlay have been further integrated with AIS and MARPA, and depth sounders, weather, and tide and current information. The evolution of the technology has been more rapid than many pundits predicted at the time the second edition of *The Radar Book* went to press.

The first, and most obvious value of radar overlay is that it makes it possible to instantly verify that the chart does not contain any positioning errors and the integrated system is working well together. If your GPS receiver is receiving signals without interference, your AIS will show the other vessels accurately superimposed on the integrated display (so long as the AIS transceiver

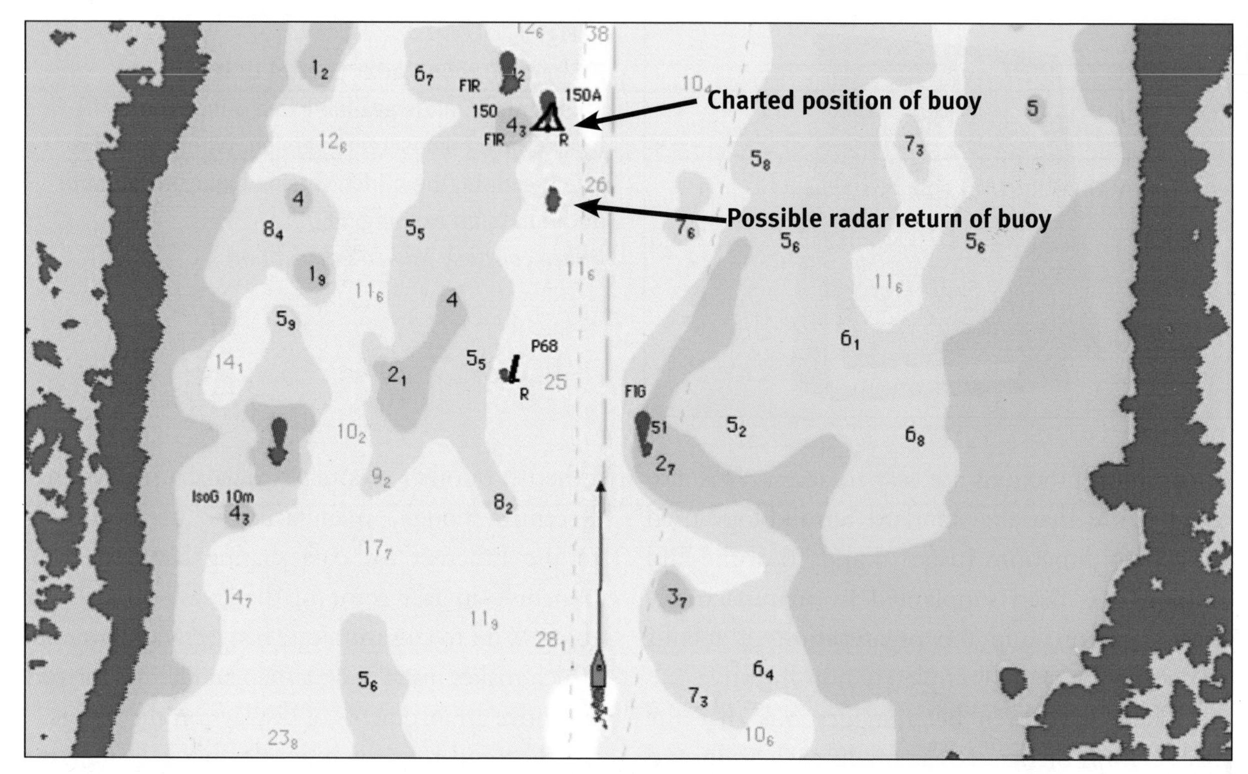

▲ **Fig. 5**

Buoy Out of Position

In the radar overlay image above, buoy 150A (arrow) is missing from its advertised position. There is no radar echo associated with the position of the buoy on the chart, but there is a return from nearby which may be the actual buoy out of position. However you should not automatically assume that this is the missing buoy--it could also be a small vessel. Remember, Rule 7(c) states "Assumptions shall not be made on the basis of scanty information, especially scanty radar information."

on the other vessel is also operating properly). If the radar is not overly cluttered with targets, the radar overlay allows the presentation of data from multiple sources in one user-friendly interface.

The combination of charts and radar provides a visual environment that enhances the operator's ability to navigate safely.

Certain data shows well on a radar display. AIS and MARPA both provide target vectors, indicating the present (and sometimes, the past) motion of targets. This type of addition to the radar display causes minimal interference, and provides valuable information to the operator. The vectors attached to each target have a length in minutes that is set by a menu choice. In other words, the addition of AIS and MARPA to the mix enhances the ability to rapidly understand other vessel activity and its relation to your own vessel—a vital function for collision avoidance purposes.

Radar overlay helps you to identify those targets that are on the chart and those that are temporary such as vessels, floating debris, birds, whales etc. When AIS-equipped vessels are displayed with their directional vectors, it is easy to tell which are the AIS targets that need to be assessed for their risk of collision. You can then turn your attention to other targets and query them with MARPA to determine which of those targets are a risk. Having

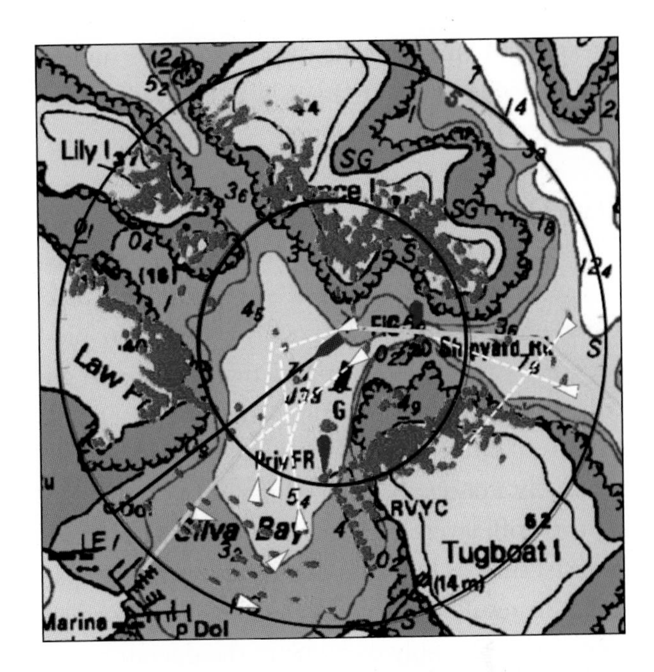

Fig. 6a ►

A Cluttered Radar Display

Overlaying radar imagery onto an electronic chart is a valuable enhancement to the navigational chart, but adding chart imagery to a radar display does not necessarily enhance the radar. This image is cluttered by AIS data and numerous small vessels, both underway and at anchor. The addition of chart imagery to this display has not improved the effectiveness of the radar for avoiding collision.

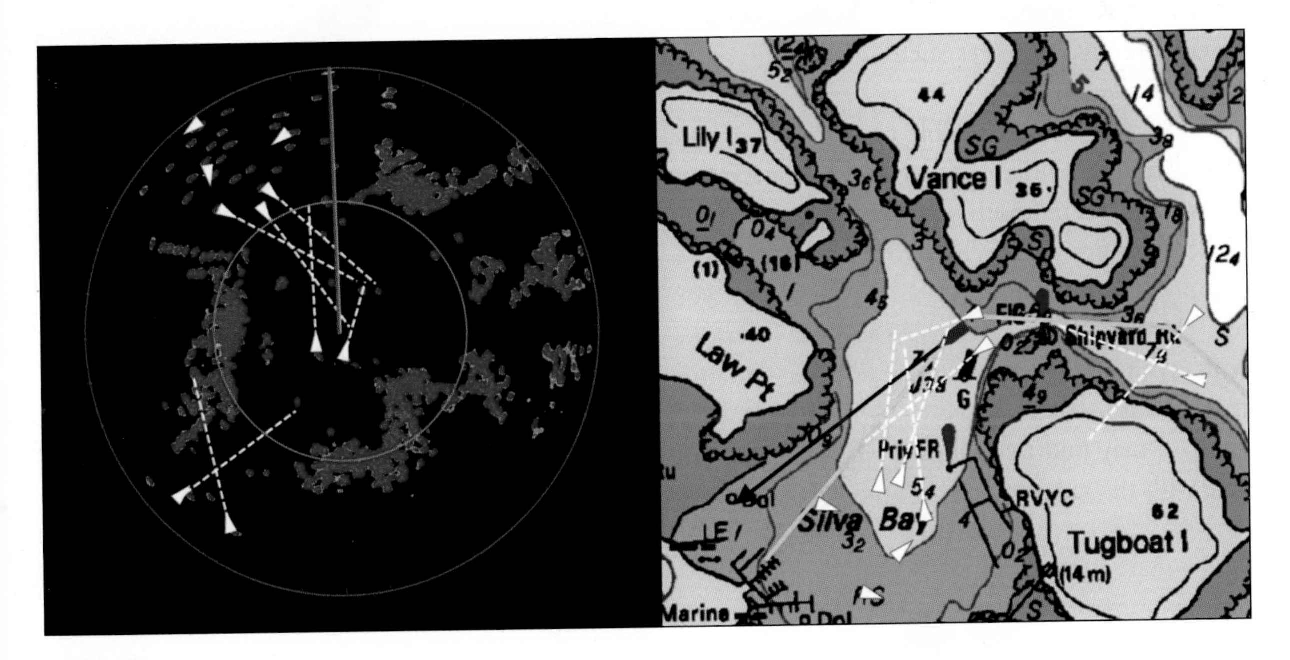

▲ Fig. 6b

Separation of Chart and Radar Displays

The same location, with radar and chart imagery displayed separately. In this case it is better to keep the radar and chart images separate. The radar image gives a much better view of the potential collision situations. The chart image gives a better appreciation of the navigation situation. Both images display AIS targets. The radar image is head-up. The chart image is north-up.

background charts on the display assists in understanding where certain targets may be headed, and thus their likely future motion.

Data Density

The presentation of so much data in one place can also be a double edged sword, for instance when there are dozens of vessels in the radar picture, all with their own predictive vector and all competing for your attention. Add to this a chart that is cluttered with additional information, especially a raster chart for which it is not possible to turn off layers of data, and numerous fixed objects, such as buoys, rocks and anchored ships, and the result is a "perfect storm" of information that can simply overwhelm the operator and render the combined imagery almost unusable. In certain circumstances such a situation can be quite troublesome.

The answer is to be able to switch to a pure radar display, while still having the electronic chart available in another window or on another piece of equipment. When you are faced with a complicated collision avoidance situation, you may find that the chart background interferes with your ability to understand the dynamic interaction between vessels.

You may find that you are far more comfortable with the radar in head-up mode when assessing other vessels' movements on radar. When radar is in head-up mode it is an ideal configuration for collision avoidance. Head-up mode is intuitive—vessels to starboard appear in the right side of the display and those to port are on the left.

However, the chart display is most intuitive when it is in north-up mode. North is at the top of the display—the way you will normally read a map or a chart. And if you are using a radar overlay to enhance your navigation, you will want to keep the radar overlay in north-up as well.

Depending on whether collision avoidance or navigation is your first priority, the ideal orientation of the radar display changes. Often you will need to switch your thinking (or your perception) rapidly from navigation mode to collision avoidance mode. At those times, it is very useful if all you have to do is move your attention from one MFD to another. If you only have one display screen, and you have to switch the display from North-up radar overlay to Head-up pure radar, then you should practice the change-over until you can do it without thinking.

North Stabilization

In order to make it possible to overlay the radar image on an electronic chart, it is necessary that both the radar image and the chart image are both oriented the same. This means that they

◄ **Fig. 7**

A Furuno C500 Flux-Gate Compass

A flux-gate compass provides precise measurements of the direction of the Earth's magnetic field, and outputs data in digital format. Normally a flux-gate is gyro-stabilized to compensate for rapid acceleration due to rate of turn or pitching and rolling.

However, it is still a magnetic compass and must be treated as such.

Courtesy Furuno USA

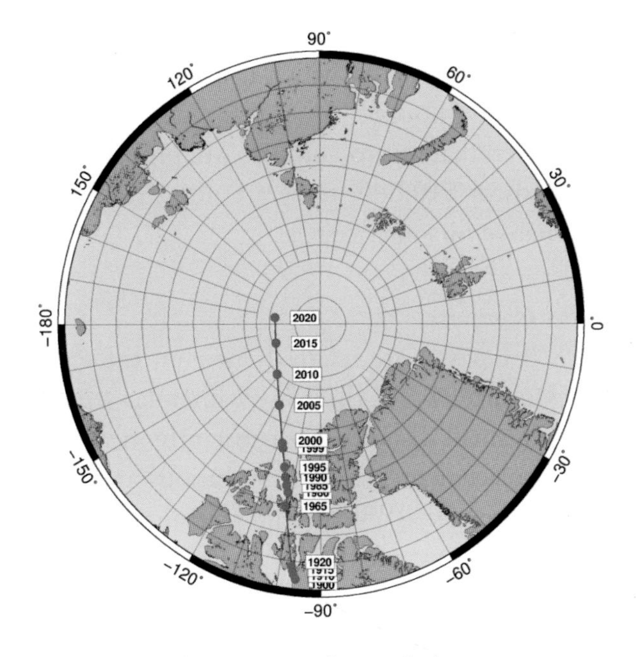

◄ **Fig. 8**
The North Magnetic Pole in Motion
Not only is the north magnetic pole moving toward Russia, but it is picking up speed. This causes the value of magnetic variation to change worldwide, with some areas changing faster than others.
Courtesy Woods Hole Oceanographic Institute

must be at the same scale, and the two images must have the same compass orientation.

With few exceptions, true north is at the top of an electronic chart. This means that the radar image must also be in north-up mode. The only way to stabilize the radar image to be north-up, is to supply it with digital compass data.

There are three possible sources of digital compass data:

- Magnetic flux-gate compass
- GPS compass
- Gyro compass

Magnetic Flux-gate Compass

Though some of the early electronic compasses were simply sensors attached to the body of a standard magnetic compass, a true flux-gate compass consists of wire coiled around a core of highly permeable magnetic material. The flux-gate directly senses the direction of the horizontal component of the Earth's magnetic field and outputs the direction in digital format.

Since a flux-gate is actually a type of magnetic compass, it is affected by the vessel's own magnetic field and nearby metallic objects. So the same cautions that apply to a magnetic compass apply to a flux-gate;

- It must be swung periodically and adjusted or compensated, especially after the removal or addition of nearby electrical or electronic equipment.
- Care must be taken to ensure that there are no tin cans, coils of copper wire or other metallic or magnetic objects in the near vicinity.
- The flux-gate should be located as low as possible and as close to the centerline of the vessel as possible to reduce horizontal and vertical accelerations to a minimum. However, you may have to find a compromise between locating it away from large metallic objects (batteries, engine block) and locating it as low as possible

Since a flux-gate compass provides magnetic direction data, in order for this data to be utilized by the radar, it must also convert from magnetic direction to true direction. Since the amount of magnetic variation is dependent on location, your MFD requires access to a database of magnetic variation for locations worldwide.

But magnetic variation changes with time. If you look at the compass rose on any paper chart, you will see that a value is given for magnetic variation at that location, but also, the rate of change per year. And herein lies a problem.

Briefly put, the magnetic variation at any location is the measure of the difference in direction of the geographic north pole and the magnetic field lines in the area. But the Earth's magnetic field is in constant motion, due to the movement of the magnetic north pole, and its speed is increasing. In the last 20 years it has moved further than the previous 100 years. As a result, it is becoming more difficult to predict the future value of variation at any point on Earth.

The accuracy of your magnetic compass may not be critical in most navigation applications. After all, it is often difficult to steer a small boat within two or three degrees of a desired heading. But when it comes to the accurate matching of a radar image to a chart display, even small errors are painfully apparent.

When it comes to maintaining the accuracy of your compass input, there are only two solutions.

- Regularly update your charts, the firmware of the flux-gate and the software in your MFD / radar.
- Use a non-magnetic compass that directly senses true north.

Gyro-Compass

These compasses operate on the two principles of gyro-stabilization; rigidity in space of a rapidly rotating object and precession. A gyro-compass requires a non-interruptible source of power. On start-up it normally takes up to five hours to become north-stabilized and if its power is interrupted for more than a moment, it will spin down to a stop, after which it must be restarted (another five hours).

Given that a gyro-compass will probably cost upwards of $10,000, these are not a reasonable alternative for small vessels.

GPS Compass

GPS compasses are relatively new on the scene. They utilize two or three GPS antennas separated by a small distance. By constantly measuring the displacement between the various antennae, a GPS compass is able to find true north directly with sub-degree accuracy. A GPS compass does require continuous power, but the amount is negligible compared to the power required to spin a gyro.

Recently the cost of reliable GPS compasses has dropped below $1,000 US, making it a very reasonable alternative to a flux-gate.

Radar Overlay Errors

(Reference page 208 of the 2nd Edition)

One of the most valuable aspects of radar overlay is that it serves as a check on the accuracy of the chart or the radar. You should learn to recognize these errors so that you are warned when there is an issue with your equipment.

Positioning Error

This error may be the result of GPS positioning error, but if so, one would expect that the error would be variable, and the radar imagery would move erratically on the chart, or not move at all. The most common cause of GPS failure is corroded or broken antenna connection, but a GPS positioning error could also be caused by multipath errors caused by reflections of the GPS signal off nearby cliffs or buildings or by masking of satellites by high mountains.

◄ **Fig. 9**
A Furuno SC30 Satellite Compass
A satellite compass refers directly to true north. There is no need to convert from magnetic to true direction.
Photo courtesy Furuno USA

If the GPS has lost satellite lock completely, both the vessel icon and the center of the radar image will come to a complete stop. However, the radar image itself will change as the vessel moves and will rapidly cease to resemble the chart display.

Other GPS positioning errors will generally be small and unstable. The result would be a mismatch between the radar image and the chart which varies regularly in both magnitude and direction.

If the problem is with the chart itself not being correctly matched to latitude and longitude, the entire chart will be shifted from its true position. The radar image, however, and the boat icon on the chart, will both be centred on their true latitude and longitude as determined by the GPS. Both the chart and the radar image will change, but will retain a constant, though inaccurate, relationship to each other.

This error may be due to the use of an older version of the chart, drawn to an obsolete datum. In well-travelled parts of North America, this kind of error is uncommon, because of the very high standard of electronic charts, especially approved government charts. However, in poorly charted areas in remote locations or in developing countries, this type of error is common.

Because it is caused by a fundamental problem with the electronic chart, there is no easy "fix" for this type of error—other than obtaining new charts. There is no way to adjust the GPS or the charts for this error. The best solution is to turn off the radar overlay and to distrust the position of the vessel on the chart background.

Scale Error

If the radar image appears to be centered on the chart accurately, but there is a discrepancy between the scale of the chart and the corresponding radar image, there may be a couple of reasons.

COG Is Not Heading

Never use a standard GPS to provide heading data. A GPS can provide Course Over the Ground (COG), but this is not heading information and will vary from the actual heading depending on the strength of the wind and current and the vessel's state of loading. A standard GPS uses a single antenna, so to provide COG it simply determines the direction between successive position fixes.

Unfortunately, when the vessel slows down or comes to a stop, the COG may begin to fluctuate wildly. As a result the radar image will rotate around the screen like a crazy thing. If the GPS is fitted with a filter that prevents it from displaying COG when at very slow speed or stopped, then the radar image will freeze in one position, even if the vessel is still slowly moving.

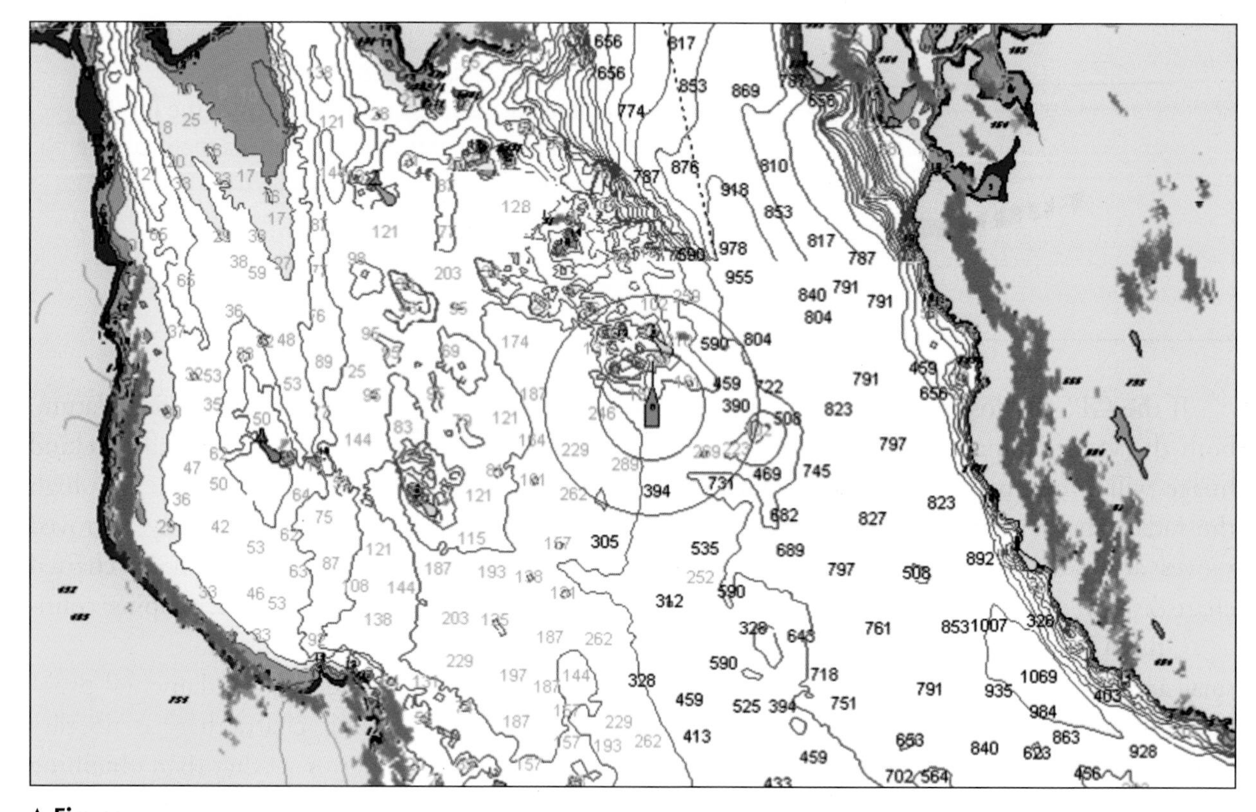

▲ **Fig. 10**
Radar Overlay Error: Chart
Though it may look like the radar imagery is in the wrong place, this error is most likely due to incorrect registration of the chart to the correct latitude and longitude.

The problem may be the result of scale conflicts between the chart and the radar. Unfortunately there is not much to be done about this other than turning off the overlay.

Zeroing error (see page 206 of the 2nd Edition) is the result of a mis-calibration of distance on the rotating time-base. The centre of the rotating time base on the PPI must be matched to the time of the beginning of transmission of the microwave pulse (except in a broadband radar). If the time ticks on the time base (which draw the range rings as the time base rotates) are shifted toward or away from the centre of the display, the radar imagery will be drawn toward the centre of the display or pushed away from it.

On some older raster-scan sets zeroing error can be eliminated by an internal physical adjustment. On a modern HD radar, the adjustment resides deep in the MFD or radar setup software. It probably requires a specialist to adjust the software on the MFD.

Rotational Error

The compass that provides data to the MFD must be properly located, adjusted or compensated. If there is a residual compass error after you have made all other adjustments and calibrations, the radar image will appear to be rotated away from the corresponding charted features.

If a flux-gate compass is the cause of the problem, the rotational error will change with the magnetic heading of the vessel, though on some

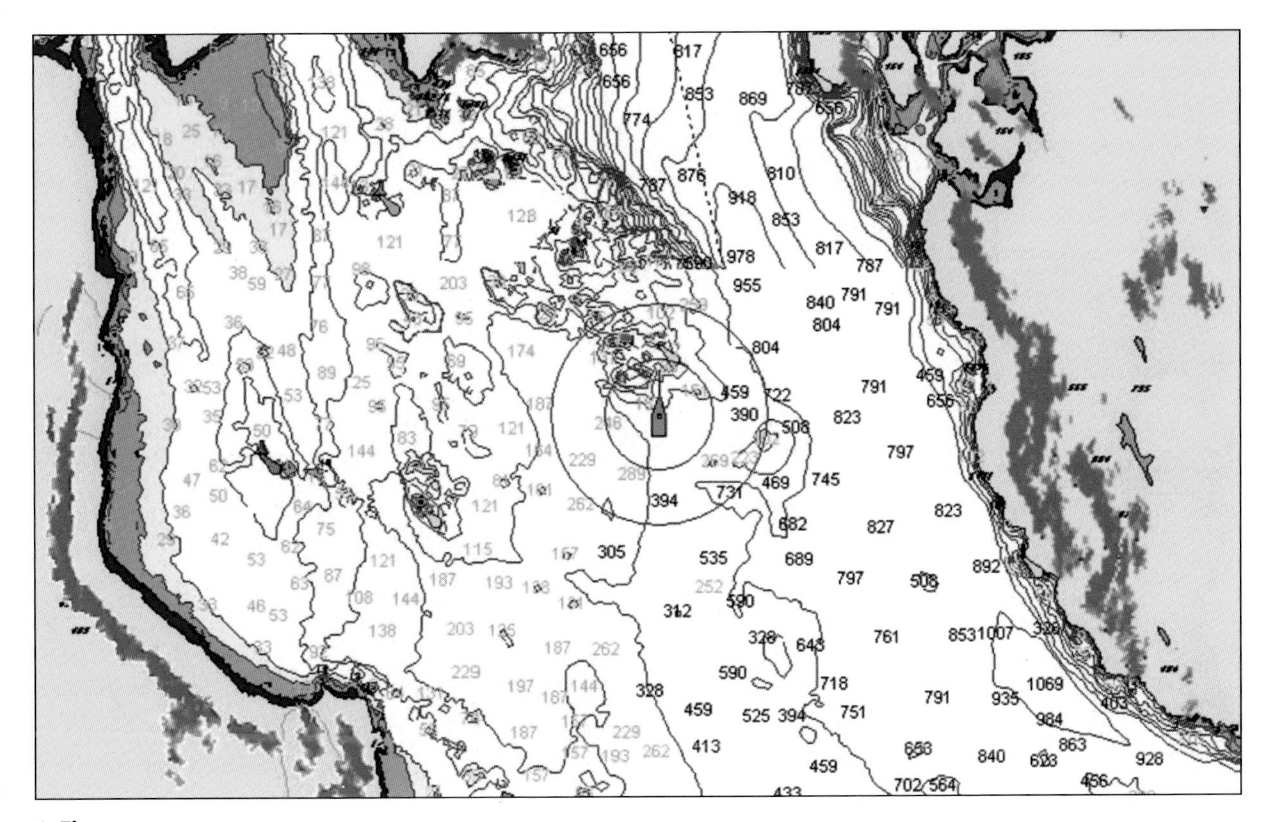

▲ **Fig. 11**

Radar Overlay Error: Scale

In this case there is a clear scale problem. This may be due to a software error in applying the same scale to the chart as it does to the radar image. However, this issue is very uncommon. The other cause may be a zeroing error. This is far less likely in a modern HD radar than in an older raster-scan unit.

headings there may be no error at all.

The only solution to a rotational error due to a compass problem is to adjust or replace the compass.

If a flux-gate compass is the compass data source, and the error does not change with heading, it is unlikely that the compass itself is the cause. You must then consider some other cause for a rotational error, such as:

- Misalignment between the radar scanner and the heading marker. This can be easily checked by lining up the bow of the vessel on a point source target such as a buoy or piling, and observing whether the image of the buoy appears dead ahead on the radar. If it does not, it should be easy enough to resolve this through an adjustment of the MFD software.
- Incorrect values for magnetic variation in the chart, MFD software or flux-gate firmware. The solution is to update the chart, firmware and / or software.

There may be times when you are aware there is an error, but you are unable to determine the source of the error. For instance, if there is only one charted object on your display, and its radar image does not match the chart. This could be the result of any of the errors identified above, or it could even indicate the object is out of position.

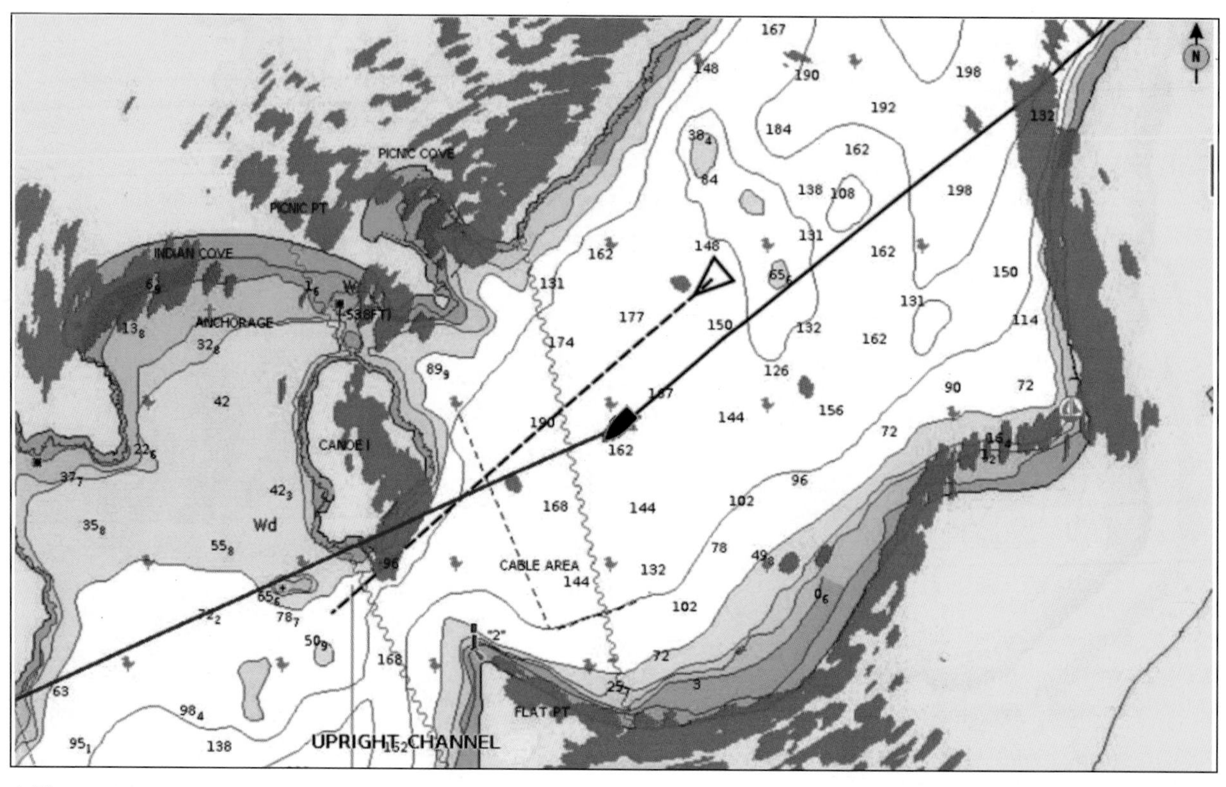

▲ **Fig. 12**

Radar Overlay Error: Rotation

A radar overlay image showing very clear rotational error. In this case the rotation was due to the flux-gate compass error. *Detail from Simrad NSS-12 MFD & 4G radar*

Scale Problems

Scale problems can also develop in the use of an electronic chart. Certain features of a vector chart may not increase in size when zooming into a problem area. Unlike the image of a series of rocks in a raster chart—which will grow larger

◄ **Fig. 13**

Fig. 13 Unknown Error

In this situation the charted feature and its echo appear to be displaced. The displacement may be due to a chart registration error or a rotational error. It is unlikely to be a scale error—in that case the echo would appear either closer to the radar or further away.

Switching to a longer range scale may help by identifying if there are any additional targets out of position. But the error might also not be apparent at the longer range. One way to get additional information is to compare the charted depth to the actual depth to determine if there is any misplacement. However, this will not help to identify a rotational error.

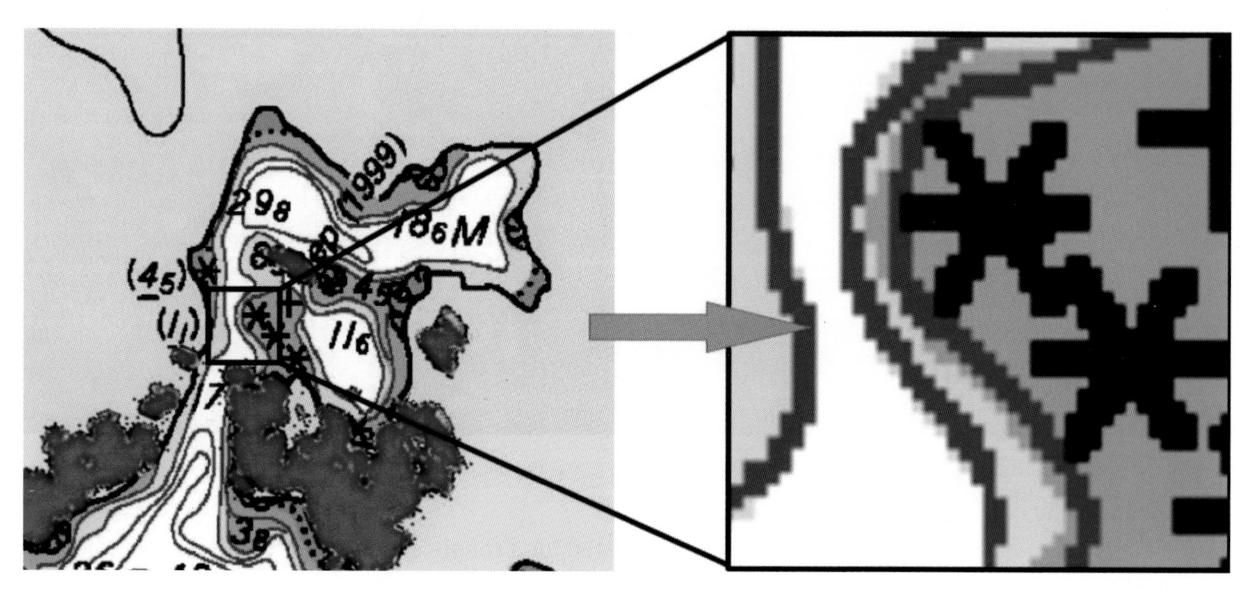

Fig. 14a

Scale Issues—Raster Chart

Though the image to the right has been over-zoomed, and the chart has lost detail definition, it is still very clear that the chart symbols for dangerous rocks cover a large portion of the right-hand image. The size of the rock symbols helps to establish the scale in effect when on extreme magnification, especially when there is no radar imagery in the frame.

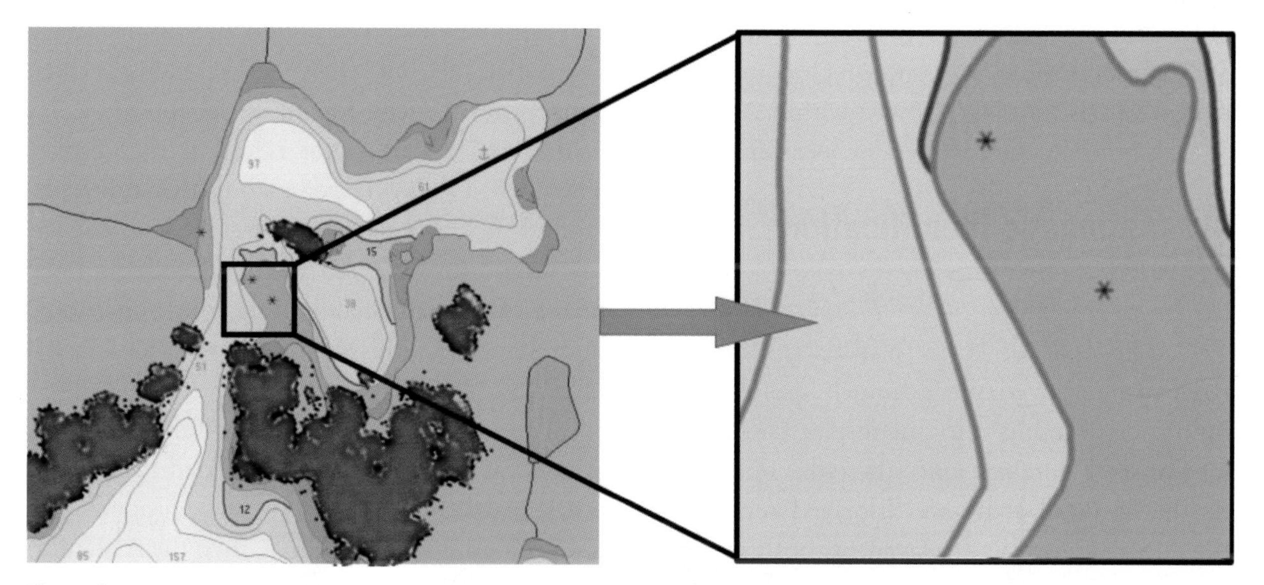

Fig. 14b

Scale Issues—Vector Chart

The same area zoomed to the same magnification as above. The chart symbols for a dangerous rock have not increased in size, possibly leading one to the erroneous conclusion that it is safe to pass between the two rocks. The scale in effect is not obvious. When zooming into the chart, it is essential to ensure that you have a good understanding of the scale involved. The best way to do this is to choose a range scale that keeps radar imagery onscreen.

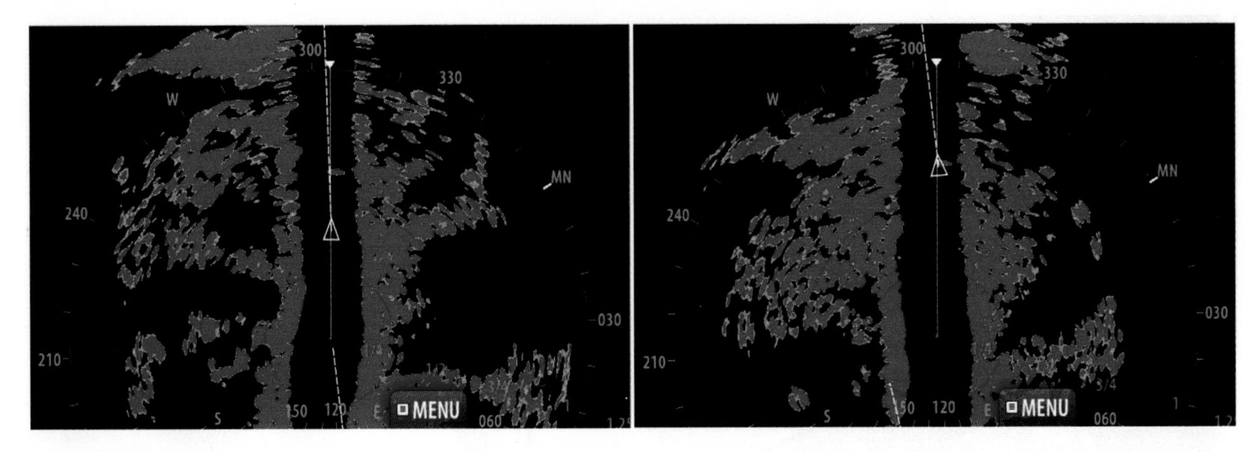

▲ **Fig. 15**

AIS Update Delay

Left, a Class B AIS on the target vessel has not been updated for a couple of minutes. The AIS icon lags behind the target image. Right, suddenly, on the AIS position being updated, the icon "jumps" forward to catch up with the radar target image. *Details from Simrad NSS-12 MFD & 4G Radar*

as you increase the magnification of the chart, symbols on a vector chart may not increase in size. This can lead to a serious misunderstanding of the scale in effect at the time.

Figure 14 shows an issue which contributed to two vessels running aground within 24 hours of each other in exactly the same location.

AIS (Automatic Identification System)

(Reference page 115 of the 2nd Edition)

The addition of AIS layers to an electronic chart, radar or radar overlay is extremely useful. If the multitude of inputs into one display clutters the screen (see Figure 6a), once the radar image and the background chart are displayed separately, the AIS data can be displayed on both without causing problems.

At the time *The Radar Book* 2nd Edition was published, Class B AIS was not approved for use in the US. This has now changed, and AIS has become widespread. However, it is still not possible to assume that every vessel is AIS-equipped. And it is still the case that some of the older Class A AIS units are unable to "see" Class B transmissions.

Class B units only update their transmissions every minute or so. On a static AIS display this is not noticeable, but when viewed against a radar image, the AIS icon for the vessel appears to lag behind the actual target echo on the display. Then, when the AIS updates, on a dynamic background such as a radar or chart, the icon appears to "jump" forward and catch up with its radar image. This can be unsettling, but you should understand that this will occur with all Class B units.

The information broadcast by an AIS is only as good as the information provided to it. If the other vessel's GPS ceases to work properly and gives out an inaccurate signal, then the AIS information will be erroneous and the location of its icon will be displaced from its associated target echo. Some vessel owners re-name their vessels without updating the MMSI associated with the unit. The result is that the name of the vessel on the AIS display will not match the registered name of the vessel. If you make a VHF call to the

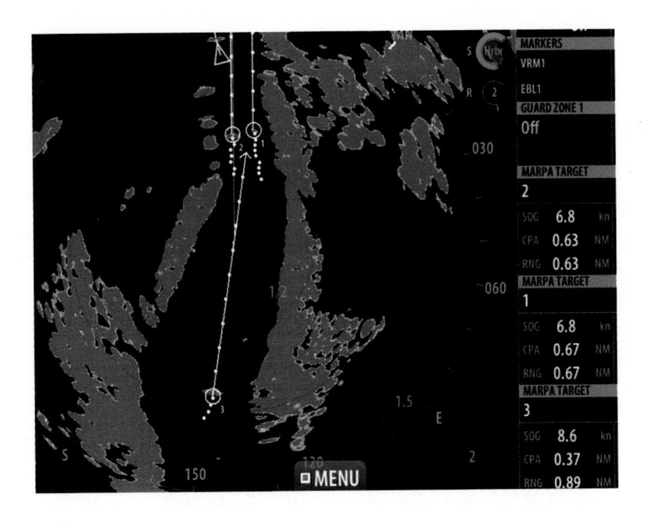

◄ **Fig. 16**
Supplementing AIS with MARPA
Of the four targets visible on this display, only one is broadcasting AIS (triangle) so the operator has captured the other three vessels with MARPA. In addition to the predicted heading vector of targets, this MARPA also shows a target's past motion with a "breadcrumb" display. *Detail from Simrad NSS12 MFD & 4G radar*

vessel named on the AIS display, you may get no answer. And you will not know that conversations overheard on VHF radio refer to that vessel.

Consequently you should be aware that AIS is not a foolproof system, and that it may not always perform as you expect.

ARPA (Automatic Radar Plotting Aid)

(Reference page 177 of the 2nd Edition)

ARPA and MARPA

Don't be confused by the two abbreviations, The difference between ARPA and MARPA is that ARPA meets the IMO standard for large international vessels; MARPA is merely a Mini-ARPA, and performs many of the same functions as an IMO-compliant ARPA, but it does not have to meet any specific standard. Consequently every manufacturer takes their own approach (there is no common standard) for MARPA.

Nonetheless, both ARPA and MARPA are tremendously useful tools for identifying the actual course and speed of another vessel, and the risk of collision. However, since they do fundamentally the same thing it will suffice to simply refer to MARPA.

MARPA can be used to assign heading vectors to targets that are not broadcasting AIS. If there are three or four targets onscreen that do not show AIS vectors, then you can supplement the visualization by capturing the non-AIS vessels with MARPA.

When MARPA is used for non-AIS targets, and both AIS and MARPA vectors are displayed, the operator will have a more complete appreciation of the movements of other vessels on the display.

Scenario	Relative Course (deg)	Relative Speed (kn)	CPA (Nm)	Time to CPA (min)	True Course (deg)	True Speed (kn)
1	3.0	0.8	0.5	1.0	7.4	1.2
2*	2.3	0.3			2.8	0.8
3	4.4	0.9	0.7	1.0	3.3	1.0
4	4.6	0.8	0.7	1.0	2.6	1.2

Table 1
In scenarios 1, 3 and 4, the target distance is 8 Nm. For scenario 2, the target distance is 1.0 Nm.

MARPA Error

Bearing Error

MARPA manages to find the course and speed of a target, and its closest point of approach, by tracking the movements of the target over a specific period of time. The IMO standard calls for ARPA to be able to resolve a preliminary estimate of target data within one minute and a complete assessment within three minutes. Needless to say, the preliminary estimate will be approximate, but it is revealing to find out just how much margin of error is permitted by the IMO standard.

The IMO ARPA standard sets out four scenarios and then establishes an accuracy requirement for the predicted motion (after 3 minutes) for each (see Table 1).

Note that this standard is for big ships, which can be steered within one degree or less. We know that when assessing the relative motion of another vessel we must maintain our own course and speed or else the results will be erroneous. So how accurate would the MARPA be when mounted on board a small vessel that is probably capable of being steered within only 3 or 4 degrees? The answer is "Significantly less accurate than the standard!"

There are many reasons for this level of inaccuracy. Certainly beam width distortion of the target echo means that it will be difficult to get an exact fix on the bearing of the target. But more important than the bearing distortion is the variability of the target's shape on the display.

As anyone has noted who has watched a vessel target on a radar, the target may change shape over time—sometimes it may change shape significantly with each sweep of the time base. When the shape of the target changes, its geometric centre changes as well. Since the radar software determines the bearing of the target to be the bearing of the geometric centre of its echo, this means that the MARPA will see the target as changing its bearing on a constant basis. Add this uncertainty to the variability of your own vessel's heading, and you can see where much of the MARPA error comes from.

This means that:

1. you can depend on the MARPA for an approximate indication of the motion of other vessels, but be prepared for the target data to change, possibly very rapidly.
2. it is a good idea to use MARPA for non-AIS targets. Though AIS may have errors as well, it is generally more accurate than a small vessel MARPA.

Target Switching

When two targets approach each other very closely, so that their echoes merge temporarily, they may switch MARPA identities. If that happens, each target will display erroneous information, until the continuous tracking of the MARPA provides new target data. This may take up to three minutes.

A MARPA identity may also be switched with a land mass, if the target gets so close to a fixed object or shoreline. In that case, you will have to cancel tracking and re-acquire the target.

True and Relative Vectors

Many (if not all) of the MARPAs available today are capable of displaying relative motion or true motion heading vectors. As a general rule, MARPA and AIS will default to true motion vectors. This will be the case whether or not the radar is in true motion or relative motion mode. So what is the difference?

When the radar is in relative motion mode (either north-up or head-up) the basic rules of relative motion are that

1. fixed targets move in the direction opposite to the direction of motion,

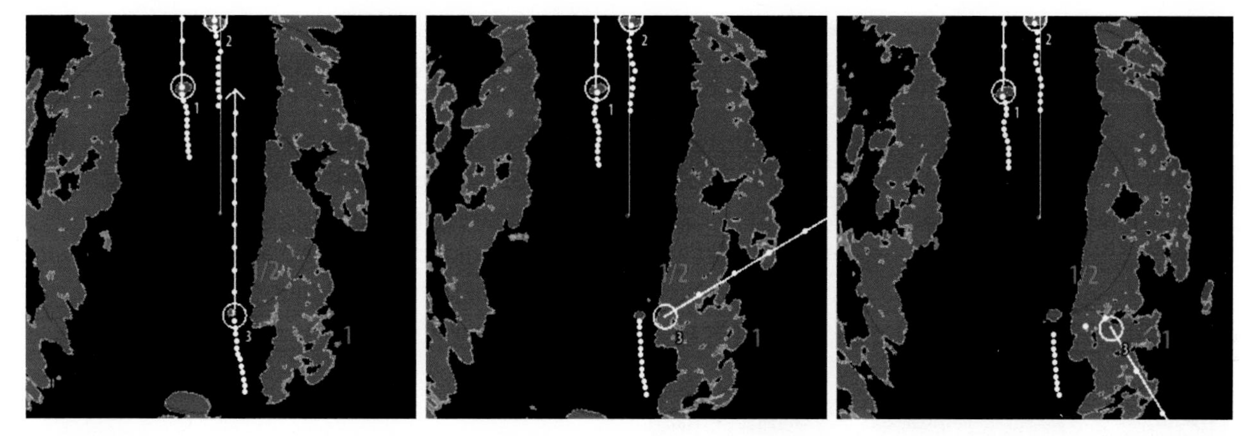

▲ **Fig. 17**
MARPA Target Switching
Target #3 (bottom of display) has approached so close to shore (left) that its MARPA identity is captured by the shoreline (centre). The MARPA focuses on different places in the shoreline as it tries to find the geometric centre of its new target. The result is that the MARPA icon and vector wander around within the shore echo (right). Target #3 must be cancelled and re-acquired. *Details from Simrad NSS-12 MFD*

2. moving targets move in the direction of their relative motion, and
3. targets on a collision course move directly toward the centre of the display.

Therefore the relative motion vector of a dangerous target would point toward the centre of the display, but the true motion vector of the same target would point in the direction of its observed COG (course over the ground)

Typically a MARPA or AIS vector is ticked at intervals. These intervals are the same for every target on the screen. If the end of your vessel's heading vector and the end of the target vessel's vector coincide, or if the two vectors cross at a common number of ticks, this indicates a potential collision.

Sometimes your own vessel will not have a ticked heading vector, and this makes it more difficult to establish if there is a potential risk of collision, so it is still necessary to assess potentially dangerous targets by setting the EBL on them, to see if there is actual risk of collision. However, the only targets you need to check are those whose true motion heading vector crosses your own heading marker.

Remember you can query any target to determine its data and risk of collision. MARPA and AIS also provide alarms, and assessments of risk of collision, so you don't need to depend on your own visual assessment of the situation. The equipment will help you to make these assessments. And if in any doubt, put the EBL on a target and see if its relative motion is toward the centre of the display.

So why not go on relative motion vectors all the time? The answer is found in the first rule of relative motion above. If fixed targets move opposite to the heading marker, then AIS vessels that are transmitting while tied to a dock will have a vector pointing opposite to your own direction of motion. If you are passing a marina full of vessels, likely several of their owners will have forgotten to switch off their AIS, and your radar display will be cluttered with relative vectors.

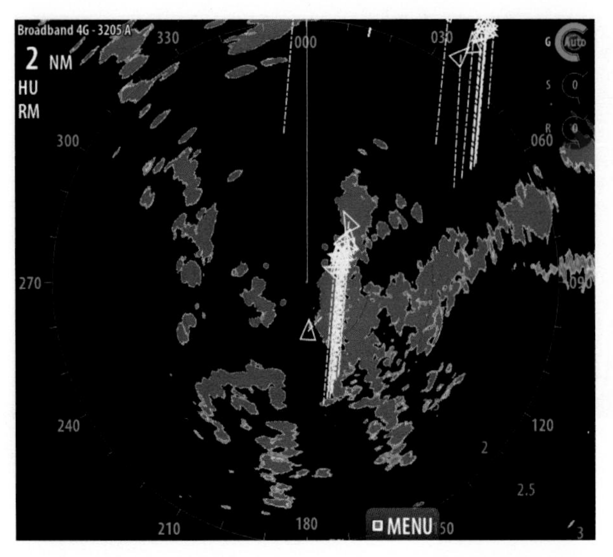

◄ **Fig. 18**

Relative Motion Vectors of Stationary Vessels

Stationary AIS targets, such as vessels in a marina will still have a relative motion with respect to your own vessel. Therefore their relative vectors will indicate movement opposite to your own vessel's direction of motion. In this situation there is a current setting to the right, which causes the fixed target's vectors to indicate slightly to the left. *Detail from Simrad NSS-12 MFD & 4G radar*

Ironically it is much more intuitive to show true motion vectors on a relative motion display. Just remember that you may still have to query the relative motion of a target. And also remember that when switching from relative motion vectors to true vectors, both AIS and MARPA vectors are normally switched together, so switching from true to relative vectors on the MARPA will also switch the AIS vectors and result in the problem set out in Figure 18.

The New Technology

HD Radar

Every radar manufacturer now offers HD (high definition) radars. HD radars generally provide sharper and more detailed images (as one would expect), but they also offer a number of other features, such as sophisticated auto-gain, auto-STC, auto-FTC and interference rejection capabilities and beam-sharpening (which reduces beam-width distortion).

One way in which HD radar provides such sharp imagery is by suppressing weaker echoes and accentuating stronger echoes. Somewhere in the software for your set there may be a "threshold" adjustment. If the threshold is set too high, only the strongest returns will be displayed. If it is set too low, it allows most returns to be displayed and defeats the purpose of having an HD display in the first place.

Auto-Gain, Auto-STC and Auto-FTC

When I used to teach radar courses to recreational or commercial boaters, I made the point that automatic gain, STC and FTC may be convenient features, but in my experience, a well-trained operator could always adjust a radar better than the automatic software. But in recent years it has become more and more difficult to exceed the capabilities of a modern HD radar.

Now I have finally met my match. Though there may be times when the automatic features fail to perform perfectly, it is usually under extremely difficult conditions, and questionable whether a reasonably adept operator could do better. However, there are times in heavy weather when the automatic filters eliminate all clutter, and it is impossible to tell if there are small targets hidden in the clutter. During such conditions it is useful to be able to filter out most, but not all, of the sea clutter and look for solid echoes within the clutter.

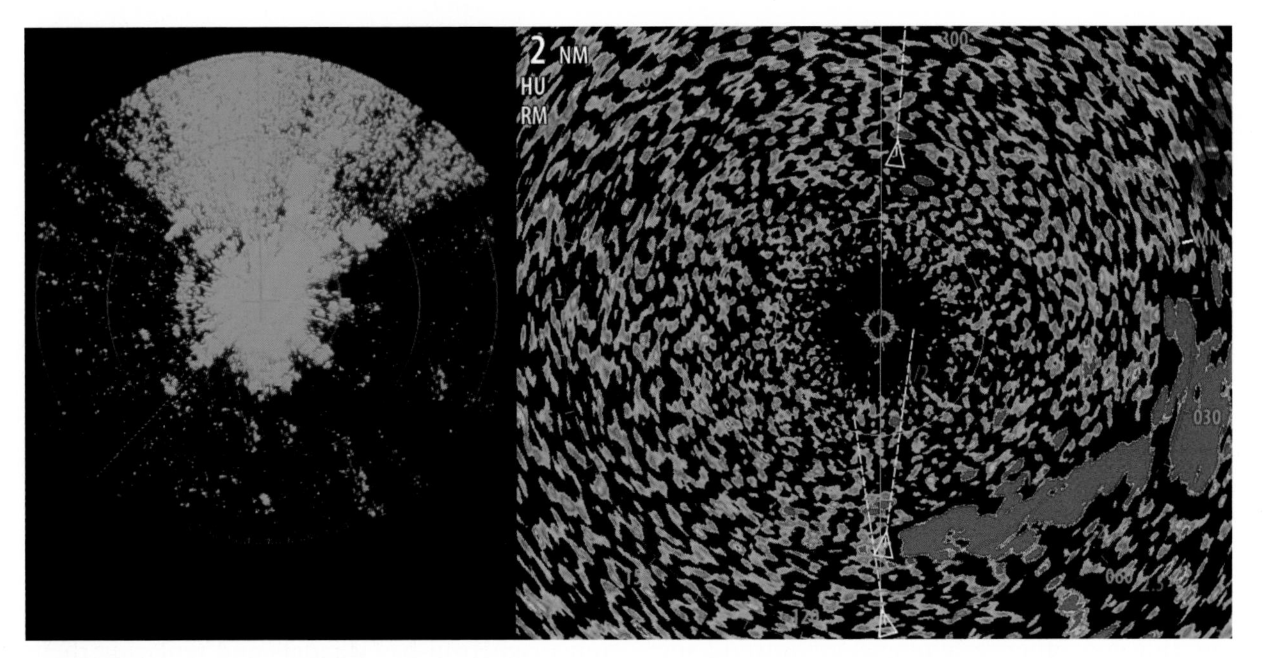

▲ **Fig. 19**
Threshold
To the left a Furuno raster-scan non-HD radar, circa 1998. To the right a detail from a Simrad 4G HD radar display.

On both radars the gain is set far too high. The older raster scan radar simply displays all the interference from very weak to very strong and every degree in between. The HD radar, however, has suppressed the light interference and accentuated the strong interference. The result is the peculiar "blobby" pattern that remains. As the gain is decreased, more and more of the strong interference is suppressed, until the remaining image is very clear and devoid of interference.

Though every manufacturer has a model of HD radar, there is no common standard, and consequently it is difficult to compare the features of different models, because the features are often very different. And when the features of two models are the same, they are often named differently, which simply adds to the confusion.

The common feature of HD radar from different manufacturers is that it is a digital technology. The difference between HD radar and raster-scan radar is the same as the difference between VHS video-tape and DVD video-disc. Where the raster-scan radar takes an analog signal and converts it to a video signal, the HD radar goes one step further and converts the returning echoes to digital information.

The interesting thing about HD radar though, is that it does not introduce any fundamentally new concepts. Digital signal-processing technology has been available for years, but without digital data to process, it had very limited applicability to marine radar. The performance improvements that became possible with HD technology are totally dependent on the conversion of the analog signal to digital data.

Once the radar echoes are converted to digital data, it is possible to apply the power of modern computer technology. It is in the processing of the returned radar signal that HD radar truly makes its mark. This trend began around the time of the publication of the second edition of *The Radar Book*, and continues to this day and

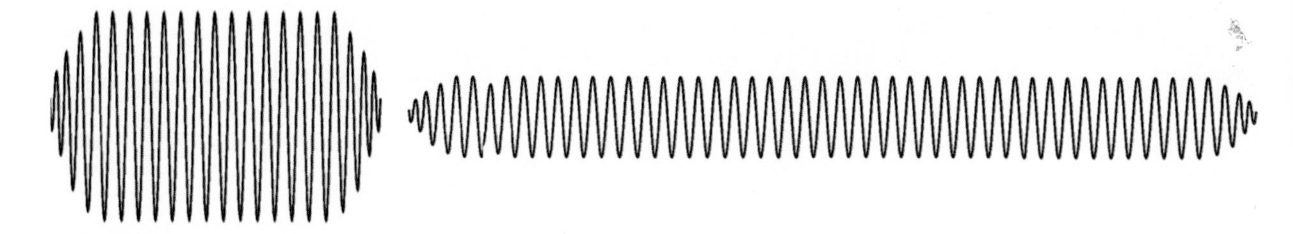

▲ **Fig. 20**
Pulse Comparison
The total energy in these two pulses is the same.
High peak power and short duration = Low peak power and long duration.

into the future. It is unclear, how much improvement is possible with this type of signal processing. But now other technologies are introducing improvements as a result of fundamental changes to the nature of the radar pulse itself.

Solid State Radar
The End of the Magnetron

(Reference page 53 of the 2nd Edition)

Just a few short years ago, all small vessel marine radars were still sending out signals generated by magnetrons—crude devices that have been the basis of radar technology since radar was first developed in the 1930s, but now the age of the magnetron is coming to an end. (Though they are still used in microwave ovens.)

Magnetron emissions are non-coherent—in other words, they cannot be confined to a narrow bandwidth. The radio frequency emissions spill over into other frequencies, making those frequencies unavailable for other purposes. Magnetrons also consume large amounts of power. They are capable of generating short, high-power bursts of RF energy, which made them perfect for radar technology. But they have had their day.

At the time of writing the first edition of *The Radar Book,* the International Maritime Organization had begun the process of phasing out magnetron-based radars and replacing them with solid state technology. This process is still ongoing.

Solid state circuits are capable of generating a coherent microwave signal with a very specific frequency. The resulting signal differs from a magnetron-based signal in the same way that the light from an incandescent bulb differs from a laser beam. But solid state circuits are not capable of generating high-power pulses of energy. Instead they are more suited to the generation of a steady stream of microwaves.

Target detection at long range relies on the total energy in the radar pulse. Therefore a low-power pulse from a solid state radar can contain the same amount of total energy, and detect targets at long ranges if the individual pulses are broadcast for a longer period of time.

The result of using low-power solid state circuits is that they use less energy in total, and so the total energy consumption of a modern solid-state radar is less than half of that of a magnetron-based radar. Another advantage is that solid state radars do not have to "warm-up". Therefore they "wake up" instantly, and do

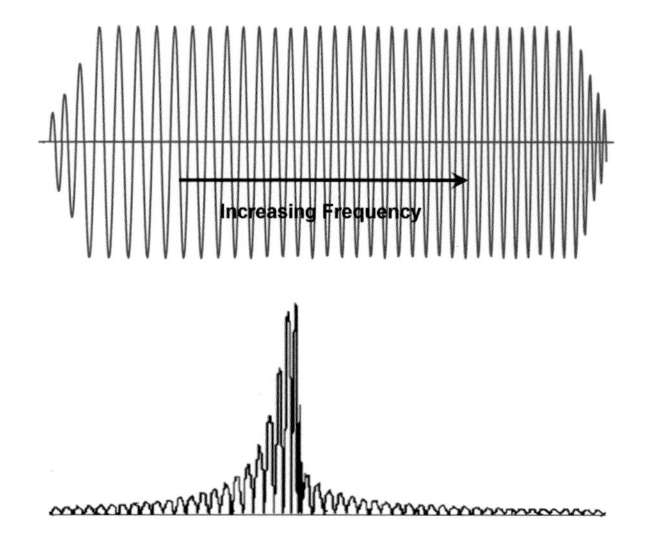

◄ **Fig. 21a**
A Frequency Modulated CHIRP before Compression

◄ **Fig. 21b**
The Same FM CHIRP after Compression

not have to be left on standby. This, combined with their low-energy consumption, makes them ideal for offshore sailors, especially if they are making occasional scans for ships while sailing on battery.

Pulse Compression Radar

Until the development of solid-state radars in the last few years, all the improvements arose out of different techniques for processing the incoming signal, but the manner of generating the outgoing microwave pulse had not changed for more than half a century.

However, when manufacturers started to work with solid state circuits, they could not ignore the fundamental limitations of those circuits for generating microwave pulses. So they had to accept low-power pulses, and broadcast them for a longer time. But the problem with that solution was that the range resolution and minimum detectable range of pulse radar depends on having a short pulse length. Obviously something had to be done.

For many years, both military radars and civilian depth sounders have employed "CHIRP" technology, and it was this technology that provided the answer. A CHIRP is simply a **C**ompressed **H**igh **I**ntensity **R**adar **P**ulse. The CHIRP begins its life as an extra-long pulse, with very specific characteristics. In a Frequency Modulated CHIRP, the frequency of the microwaves is increased (or decreased) as it is being generated, so that the CHIRP contains a range of frequencies (and wavelengths) and no two waves in the CHIRP have the same frequency.

After the CHIRP finds a target and is reflected back to the antenna, the echo contains the same range of frequencies as the original CHIRP. A matched filter is applied to the returning pulse, and as a result, the pulse collapses to reveal the true echo within. The result is a very short waveform, which simulates the effect of a very short pulse.

As shown on pages 82 to 85 of the 2nd Edition, anything that simulates a short pulse will also have the effect of increasing range resolution and thus increasing the clarity of the image. In the case of CHIRP radars, the increase in the pulse length necessary to provide enough energy to penetrate the atmosphere is more than offset by the apparent reduction of the pulse length by compression of the returning target echo. It is by this means that modern CHIRP radars are able to offer superior range discrimination—superior to the range discrimination offered by most conventional pulse HD radars.

Pulse compression radars are also able to deliver a shorter minimum range scale than conventional pulse radars. For instance, the Raymarine Quantum radar has a minimum range scale of 1/16th Nm (380 ft or 115 m), whereas most conventional pulse radars can offer only 1/8th Nm minimum range scale.

Pulse compression radars are now offered by all the major manufacturers. Within a very short time it is likely that conventional pulse radars will no longer be available. After all, it didn't take long for electronic cameras to replace film cameras.

Broadband Radar

In 2009, Navico released the Simrad BR24 broadband radar, and changed the landscape of small boat radar forever. The broadband radar challenged the entire industry not only because it used solid state circuits to generate the radar signal, but also because it abandoned the principle of pulse radar completely, and instead broadcasts a continuous wave frequency modulated (CWFM) signal.

The broadband radar broadcasts continuously—there is no pulse of energy—and therefore its peak power is extremely low indeed. In fact, the peak power in the CWFM transmission is probably equivalent to that of a cell phone. Thus Navico advertised it as the world's first "huggable radar". No longer would users have to worry about avoiding the radar beam. If it was so low powered, it could be mounted anywhere

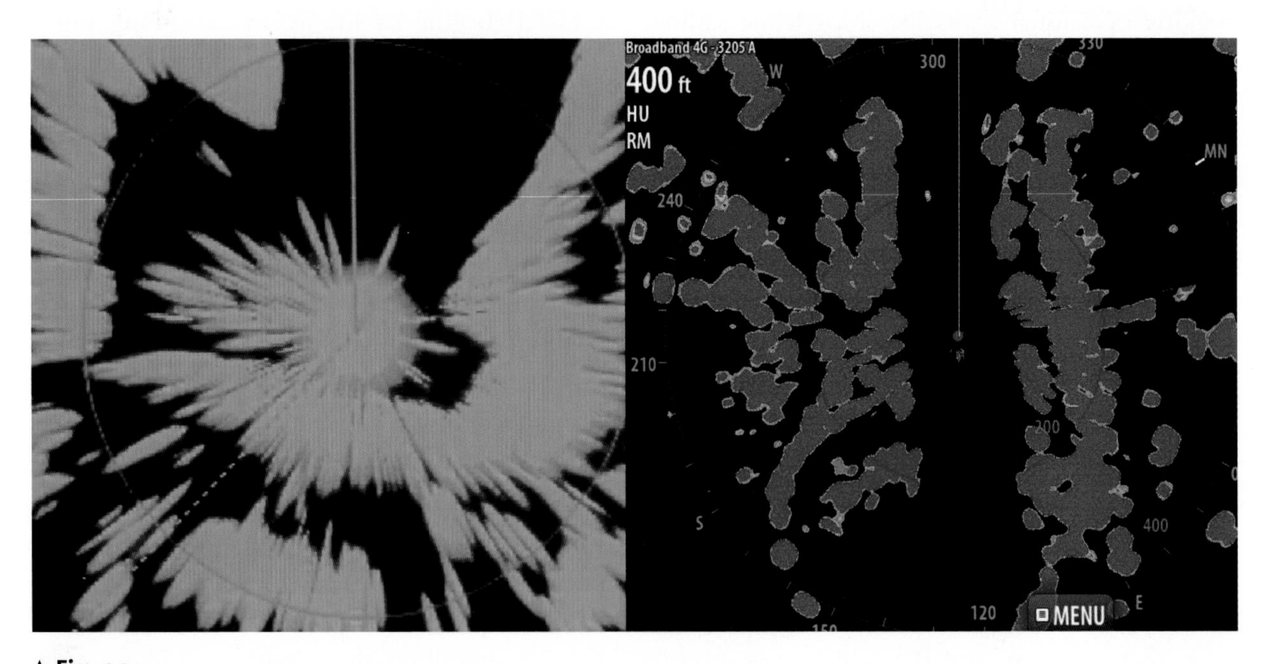

▲ **Fig. 22**

Comparison of two radar displays enlarged to the same scale

Above left, a conventional Furuno raster-scan pulse radar display at 1/8 Nm scale, circa 1998. It is difficult to identify any detail in the image. The main bang obscures about ¼ the diameter of this portion of the display. Above right, a Simrad 4G broadband radar screen-capture at 400 ft (120 m) range scale. The raster-scan image has been enlarged x 2 to be at the same scale as the broadband radar display, which shows fine detail and has no main bang.

on a small boat without worrying about irradiating the crew. In its abandonment of the pulsed signal, the broadband radar represents the most revolutionary variation since the invention of radar in the 1930s.

The Main Bang

A pulse radar cannot broadcast and receive at the same time. So, for the duration of the broadcast phase a radar is incapable of receiving a signal. If the radar is broadcasting at its shortest range, the pulse length (and thus the duration of the broadcast phase) is probably between 0.1 and 1.0 microseconds.

Since the speed of light (and radar transmissions) is approximately 300,000 km/sec (300 million metres/sec) then, during the broadcast of 0.1 microsecond pulse, the signal travels about 30 metres (100 ft). Before the radar can receive echoes it must switch to receive mode, and this takes another fraction of a microsecond. Therefore the lag in reception from the time of the beginning of the transmit phase is probably more like 60 metres (200 ft) than 30 metres.

This means that the leading edge of the echo from a target less than 30 metres (100 ft) away will have travelled less than 60 metres (200 ft) from the antenna to the target and back again, and will strike the antenna before the radar has started to listen for echoes. Because the radar can't detect anything at this close range (except the noise of its own broadcast) a small circle of light appears around the centre of the display. This is known as the main bang. Its radius is equal to half the pulse length (plus switching time) and so the main bang gets bigger as you switch to longer and longer ranges.

When the radar does switch to receive mode, it will immediately detect the echo, but it will have no way to determine when the leading edge of the echo struck the antenna, so it will simply place the echo directly around the centre of the display. This makes it impossible to separate the main bang from the actual echoes received.

Because the broadband radar broadcasts (and receives) continuously, it is equipped with two separate antennas, one for sending and one for receiving. The result is that it has no main bang because it is "listening" all the time. And because

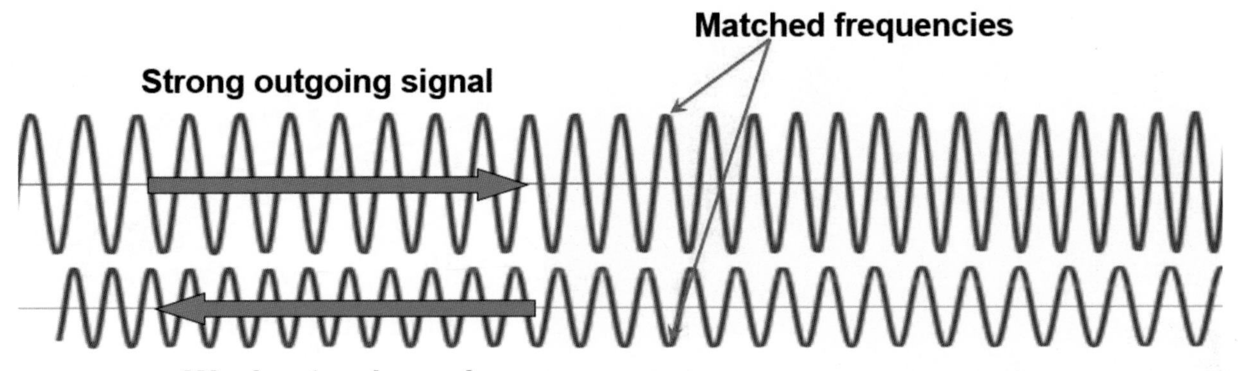

▲ **Fig. 23**
Frequency Matching
The hyper-sensitive broadband radar is able to identify the return time of a specific frequency embedded in the target echo, and thus measure distance to the target.

it transmits a low-power signal, it is not overwhelmed by the noise of its own transmissions.

Frequency Matching

Since the radar sends out a continuous signal, one might wonder how it is able to measure distance, since it does not employ pulses at all. So how can the radar measure the time it takes for the echo to return from a target, if the echo of the target is continuous as well?

The answer lies in the frequency modulated signal which continuously cycles through a very specific range of frequencies. The cycle is long enough to allow the signal to travel out to any potential target and back again without repetition. The radar then employs "frequency matching" technique to determine the time offset between the broadcast and reception times of that specific frequency. Since time equals distance, the radar then knows the distance to the target.

The bearing to the target is measured in the conventional manner, by painting the "pip" on the radar display at the same bearing that the antenna is pointing at that time.

Since the radar is not simply tracking the return time of the entire pulse, but is actually measuring the return time of a specific frequency within the echo, the distance measurement is far more precise than in a conventional pulse radar. The obvious result of this is significantly improved range resolution and clarity of the radar imagery at short ranges. However, the vertical and horizontal beam-widths are basically the same as for any small radome. Therefore bearing resolution and distortion are not affected.

Minimum Detection Range

Unlike a conventional radar, a radar without a main bang is not prevented from seeing detail at very close range. Where most pulse radars have a

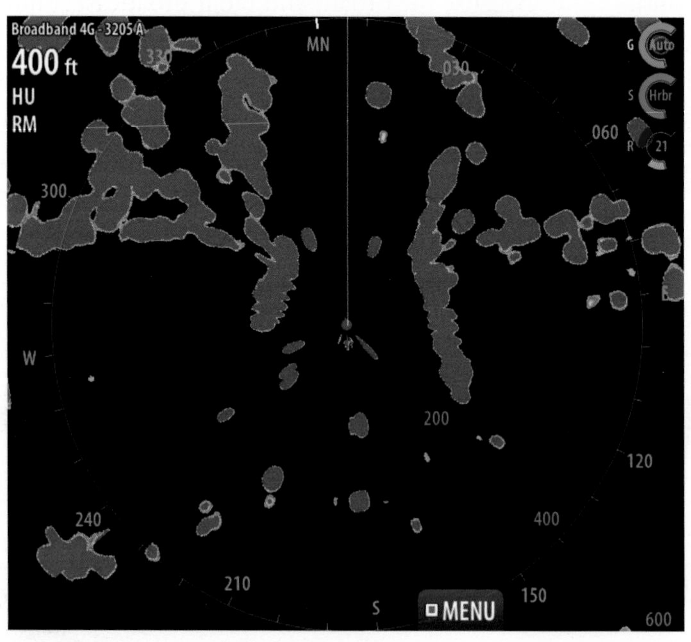

▲ **Fig. 24a**

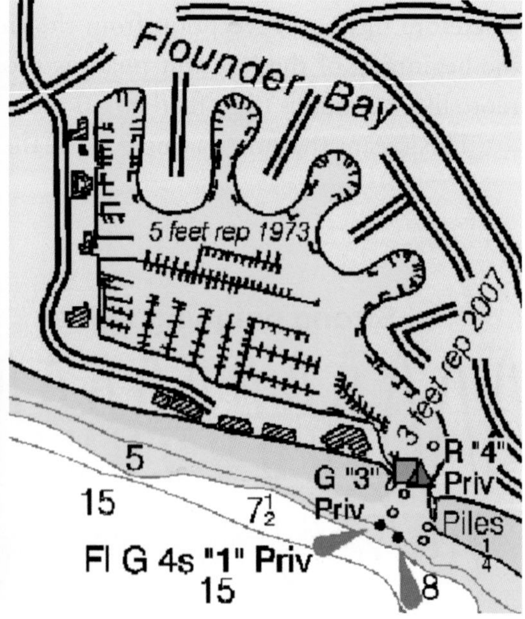

▲ **Fig. 24b**

Broadband Radar on 400 ft Range

A series of pilings define the entrance to Flounder Bay (shown at the bottom right of the chart detail.) The image above left was captured by a 4G Simrad broadband radar set to 400 ft. (120 m) range scale. The individual pilings leading to the entrance are each clearly visible less than 100 feet away from the radar antenna.

minimum range scale of 1/8 Nm (760 ft or 230 m), the broadband radar has a minimum range scale of 200 feet (60 m)—allowing the radar to identify targets at extremely close range. The specification for the 4G broadband radar (the latest model) is an unprecedented minimum detection distance of 6 feet (1.8 m)—far less than the length of the vessel it is mounted on.

Generally, most boaters with broadband radars don't find the 200 foot (60 m) range very useful. One might think that this short a range scale would be useful in navigating around a marina, but when the visibility is less than 200 feet (60 m), it is still far more effective to use one's eyes than to depend on a radar. However, the 400 foot (120 m) range scale can be very useful in tight quarters for identifying markers.

Characteristics of Broadband Radar

Every new technology has its advantages and disadvantages. Along with the cutting edge capabilities shown above, broadband radar has disadvantages as well.

Due to its extremely low power, broadband radar exhibits inferior target detection at long range—more than 8 to 10 Nm. Even though it is advertised as a 24 Nm radar, only the strongest targets are able to return useable echoes from beyond 12 Nm. This means that its ability to detect landfalls and storm cells at long range is compromised.

Coastal boaters on the other hand, may not require long-range capability for navigation. GPS provides a much more exact capability for managing landfalls and in most inshore navigation situations, a radar that is reasonably sensitive up to 10 or 12 Nm is all that is needed.

Because there is no detectable pulse in the continuous broadcast, it is unable to trigger RACONs or SARTs (Search and Rescue Transponders).

In summary;

Advantages

- Broadcast power is very low—less than most cell phones
- Wide variety of mounting options (virtually no radiation danger)
- No main bang
- Very short minimum detection distance (6 ft. or 1.8 m)
- Excellent detection of targets at short ranges (better than other radars up to 3 Nm)
- Has HD software for advanced signal processing, auto-STC and FTC, etc

Disadvantages

- Beyond medium range, its ability to detect targets is reduced.
- Will not trigger RACONs or SARTs.
- Sensitive to interference from radars on nearby vessels.

It remains to be seen if the popularity of the broadband radar will continue, or whether it will be edged out of the market by CHIRP radars (even Simrad offers a version of a CHIRP radar).

Broadband radar is probably not suitable for offshore sailors but it works well in coastal navigation, and it excels for very close quarters navigation.

One thing is certain however; as of the date of this writing, the broadband radar is unique. It was the first small boat radar to utilize solid state technology and no other company has developed a continuous wave frequency-modulated radar since then.

Doppler Radar

As a moving body emits any form of wave, whether a sound wave or light waves, the frequency and wavelength of the waves are modified by the speed of the object.

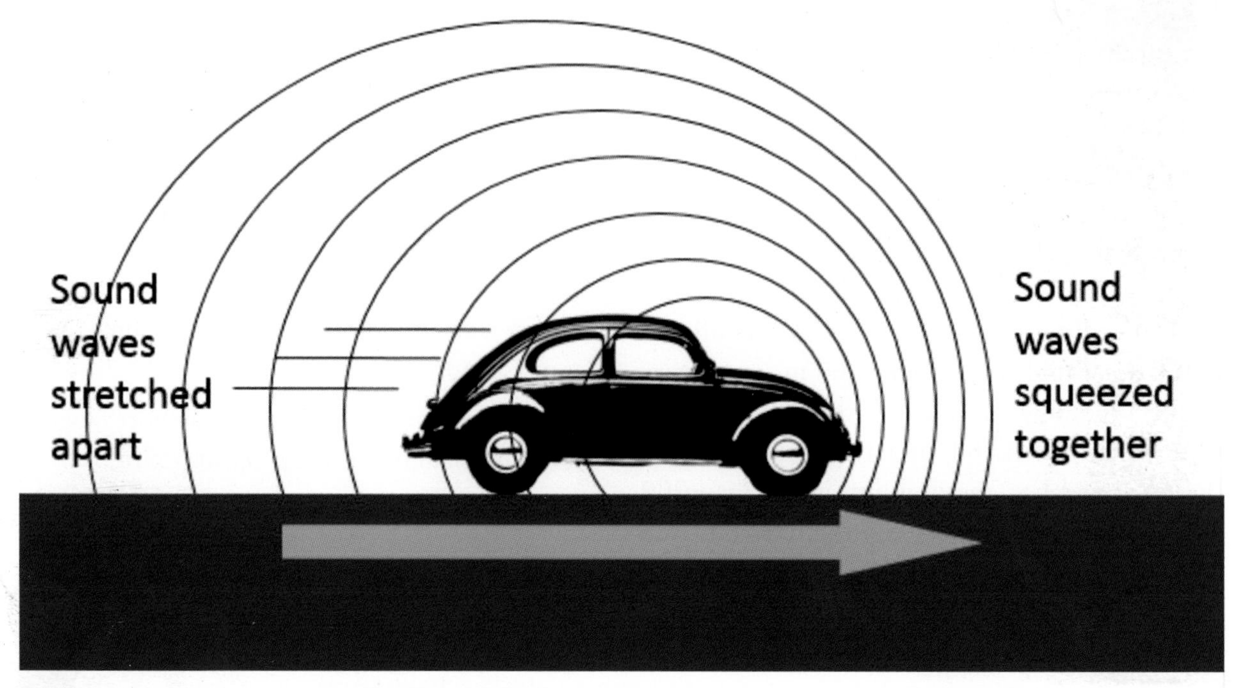

▲ **Fig. 25**
Doppler Effect
Sound waves are squeezed together in advance of the speeding car, and stretched apart behind it. This causes a stationary observer beside the road to hear a high-pitched sound as the car approaches and a lower-pitched sound once it passes. To the driver of the car, the sound does not appear to change.

The classic example is of a car blowing its horn as it approaches you as you stand beside the road. As the car approaches, the frequency of the sound is increased—because the sound waves are squeezed together ahead of the moving car—so you hear a higher pitch. But as the car passes, the sound suddenly drops in tone and is much lower-pitched as it travels away.

This increase (or decrease) in frequency and wavelength can be observed all around us in nature. Ripples in the surface of the water made as a duck slowly swims will be closer together ahead of the duck than they are behind.

The Doppler Effect is apparent whether the moving object is emitting waves itself or whether it is simply reflecting waves that have been emitted by another source. This is the principle behind Doppler logs, weather radars and a host of other technologies.

- A Doppler log broadcasts sound waves ahead of a moving vessel. These sound waves are reflected by microscopic organisms and other minute detritus in the ocean, and thus the log can determine the speed of the vessel through the water.
- A weather radar can tell if raindrops are moving toward or away from its location, and therefore, the direction the winds are blowing.
- A radio telescope measures the speed of distant galaxies receding from our own.

Until the development of modern solid-state radar with tightly controlled transmit frequencies, it was not possible to apply Doppler

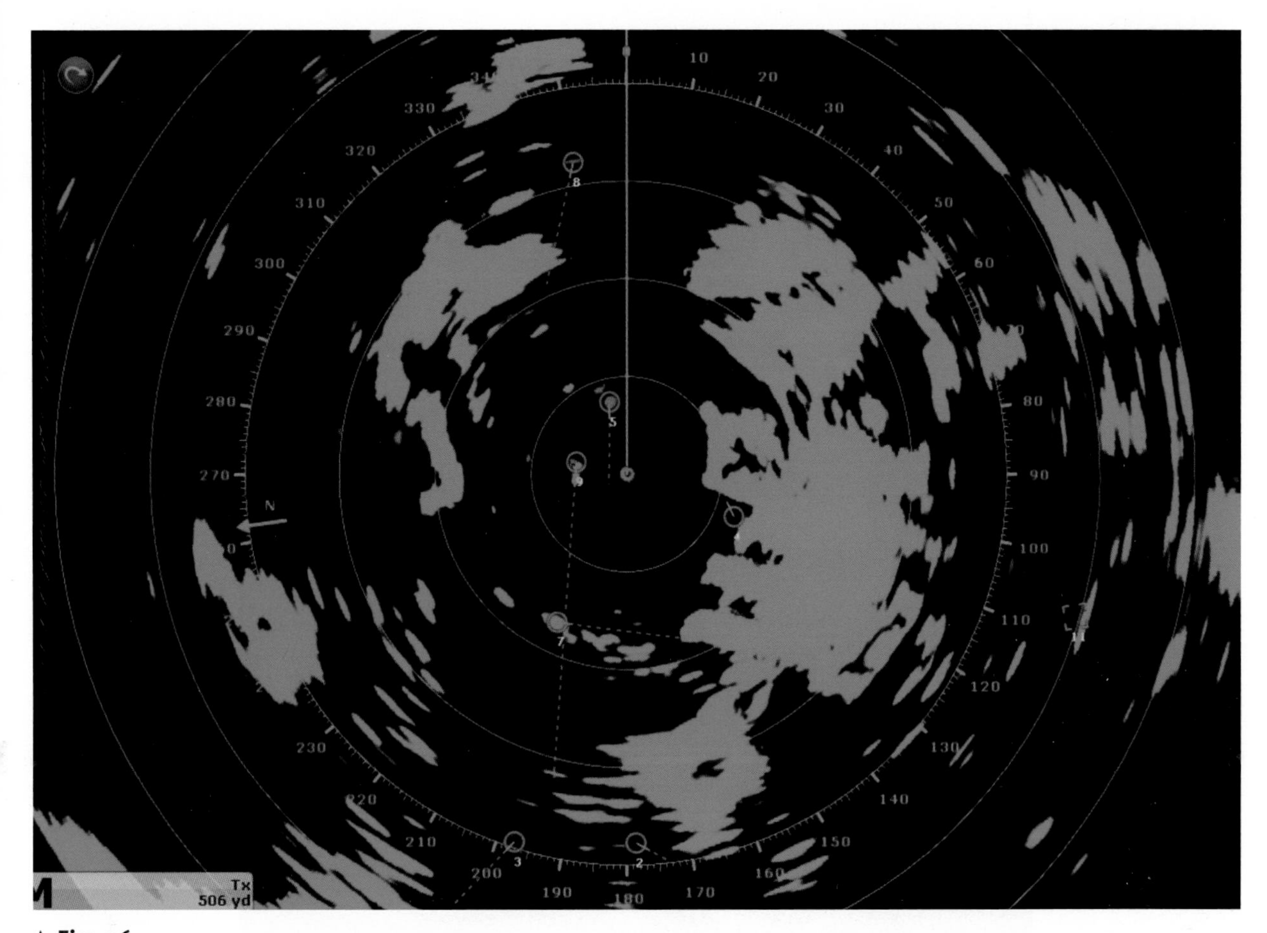

▲ **Fig. 26**

A Furuno DRS4D-NXT Doppler Radar display

With the Doppler feature of the Furuno DRS4D (Target Analyzer) active, targets moving toward the radar are coloured red. Not only does this make it possible for you to instantly recognize approaching targets, but it also identifies them even if they are located very close to a shoreline or buried in clutter.

Courtesy Furuno USA

technology to marine radar. But now that radars are capable of transmitting coherent signals with tightly controlled frequencies, it is now possible to measure the frequency shift (Doppler shift) of every target and thus the relative velocity. Not only does this allow the radar to display approaching (or receding targets) in a different colour, but it also allows the approximate velocity (speed and direction) of a target to be determined instantly—instead of waiting for software to calculate course and speed.

Doppler radar also provides superior rain-clutter and sea-clutter suppression. For decades, the military has been using Doppler radars to identify stealthy targets, and to separate these faint targets from birds and "chaff" by analysing their relative and true motion. With the development of solid-state signal generation and HD processing, this capability can now be brought to bear on the mundane tasks of small boat navigation.

At this time (January 2017) both Furuno and Garmin offer Doppler radars. But it is likely other manufacturers will soon incorporate Doppler capability in their products as well.

The Radar Book is available at nautical chandleries, West Marine, Amazon.com and the WaggonerGuide.com store for $24.95. Or call Fine Edge Nautical and Recreational Publishing at 360-299-8500 (in Canada, call Chyna Sea Ventures at 250-594-1184) to order individual and bulk copy sales.

$3.95
ISBN 978-0-9969799-7-9